C

CW00419136

Acknowledgements

At the beginning I was only going to write a short pamphlet for my wonderful grandchildren, outlining the work I had done on the so called Supergun. It was their encouragement that helped me change my mind, and produce this book. Thanks kids.
Special thanks go to Daniel for his caricatures of Saddam Hussein and Margaret Thatcher.

Last but no means least; I have to thank my wife Patricia, without whose help and support I wouldn't have got this far.
Your encouragement and enthusiasm have given me the inspiration to carry on. Lots of love and thanks 'Patty'.

Thanks to:
Alan Powell, Jane Salt and Nancy Fielder of the Sheffield Star, for all their help, in supplying me with copies of the original reports and photographs.
Sheffield City Library, Local Studies Library for pointing me in the right direction.
My mate of long standing, Brian Thompson.
An extra special big thanks goes out to our dear friend Jean Seggar (Jeannie), for all those long hours that she has helped us through and for being our computer wizard. We couldn't have done it without you Jeannie.
Many, many, thanks to you all. I am deeply grateful.

Introduction

During the past 150 years or so, much has been written about the world renowned steel works of Sheffield, since Henry Bessemer first perfected and patented the process of steelmaking in October 1855.

The skill of the engineers and forgemen, who to this day continue this tradition, is indisputable.

Apart from producing arguably the finest cutlery in the world, this great city is famous for the manufacture of the tools of war. During World War Two, many of our steel makers diversified and produced munitions for the war effort.

Barnes Wallis's 'Bouncing Bomb' was produced by Firth Browns, just one of the many acclaimed steel producers.

This plaque briefly explains the history of the now world famous 'Forgemasters, River Don Works'.

'H.M.S. Duke Of York', England's flag ship in World War Two, and which played an integral part in the sinking of Germany's seemingly unstoppable 'Scharnhorst' in Dec 1943, probably had much of her weaponry made at Firth Brown's. Three Royal Navy ships proudly bore the city's name. The first H.M.S. Sheffield was also a part of the flotilla which sank 'Scharnhorst' and saw action from the Arctic Circle to the Atlantic and in the Mediterranean.

The second was scuttled in the Atlantic Ocean, after being severely damaged by an Excocet Missile during the Falklands War in 1982 and the third was sold to Chile in 2003. The common factor that they shared was that all three had most of their fixtures and fittings made here in Sheffield; hence they were fondly nicknamed "Shiny Sheff". These are just some of the important examples of the craftsmanship of this proud and aptly named 'Steel City.' Although the number of steel works has diminished, the expertise and dedication of these men of steel, still remains.

In 1965, 105mm (millimetre) gun barrels were still being produced in the West Street Machine Shop of English Steel Corporation and at Hawk Street Planer Shop, they were machining armour plate and tank turrets under an on-going contract for the MOD (Ministry of Defence)

My contribution by comparison is small, considering the events that were to follow in 1988. I admit whole heartedly that I feel privileged and a small degree of pride that, for a short time, I was part of the elite team who innocently, almost provided Saddam Hussein with a potentially evil new toy, 'The Supergun'.

Chapter 1

Saddam Hussein's Rise to Power

Saddam Hussein was born April 28th 1937, just outside Tikrit, Iraq. Translated from the Arabic, his name means 'One who confronts'. This certainly seems to be an accurate description of his future life. His father had abandoned his mother three months into her pregnancy.

After his mother's re-marriage, Saddam had three half-brothers. As an infant, Saddam had been sent to live with his maternal uncle. His step-father did not treat him kindly or lovingly, so aged around 10 years old, he left home and went to live in Baghdad. On this occasion, he went to live with another uncle, who was the father of his future wife.

The family, like Saddam were devout Sunni Muslims. In years to come, his family in Tikrit were to become his most stalwart supporters and advisors. Saddam claimed that his uncle, a militant Iraqi nationalist, taught him many things.

Under his uncle's tutelage, he attended a nationalistic secondary school in Baghdad.

At the age of twenty, Saddam joined the revolutionary Ba'ath Party. One year later, Ba'ath Party army officers led by General Abdul Karim Qassim overthrew Faisal II of Iraq. The Ba'athists were opposed to the new Government. In 1959, Saddam was involved in the attempted United States-backed plot to assassinate Qassim.

Although he was shot in the leg, Saddam escaped to Tikrit, with the help of American C.I.A., and Egyptian Intelligence agents. After crossing into Syria, he was transferred to Beirut for a short C.I.A training course.

After re-locating to Cairo, he became a frequent visitor to the American Embassy. He lived in a well-appointed apartment, but was under observation by the C.I.A and Egyptian operatives. During his exile, he studied law at Cairo University

In 1964 Saddam returned to Iraq, but was immediately imprisoned. After his escape from prison in 1967, he soon became a leading member of his Party.

After a bloodless coup in 1968, he became Deputy to the President. He quickly became the regime's strongman.

According to Saddam's biographers, he never forgot the tensions with in the first Ba'athist government. With ruthless determination, he proceeded to maintain power and ensure programmes for social stability. Although Saddam had no military training, he quickly demanded and received the rank of a Four Star General.

For a long time, Iraq had been divided along socially ethnic, religious and economic lines, Sunni verses Shi'ite, and Arab verses Kurd.

By taking an active role in the countries domestic problems, he strove to unify and strengthen the Ba'ath Party.

He personally over-saw the modernisation of Iraq and created a strong security apparatus, to prevent coups developing with in the power structure. He strove constantly to increase support for himself throughout Iraqi society.

Iraq's oil was always central to his strategies.

During the Iraq-Iran war of 1980-1988, Iraq had used chemical weapons against Iran.

On March 16th 1988, the Iraqis had attacked the Kurdish town of Halabja. Mustard gas and nerve agents were used. And as a result 5,000 civilians were killed and a further 10,000 were seriously injured and/or disfigured.
The United States now states that Saddam had ordered the attack to reassert control of the Kurdish population of Northern Iraq. At the time, Saddam's regime blamed Iran. The United States supported that claim until the early 1990's.

The end of the war left Iraq deeply in debt. Prior to the war, Iraq and Iran both had healthy economies.

Quotes from the World Press Organisation stated that the Rumaila Oilfield that lies between Kuwait and Iraq, was disputed by both countries. During the initial 'oil boom,` Iraq had concentrated on oilfields in the north, whilst the Kuwaitis had concentrated their efforts in the Burqan oilfield in the south.

In 1989 Iraq accused the Kuwaiti government of illegal 'slant drilling` into Iraq's part of the Rumaila oilfield. It claimed $10 billion, including $2.4 million in compensation for oil stolen from the Ramaila field since 1980 by Kuwait in Iraq's section. Although Kuwait denied the accusation, Iraq instituted an 'economic warfare by military action`.

The Iraqi's justified their actions by saying that Kuwait was part of Iraq through British Imperialism. After the Anglo-Ottoman agreement of 1913, Britain split Kuwait and Iraq into two separate Emirates.

On Wednesday 25th July 1990, the Unites States Ambassador in Iraq, April Glaspie asked the Iraqi High Command to explain about their military preparations, including the massing of Iraqi troops on the Kuwaiti border.

The United States Ambassador said that Washington "was inspired by friendship, not confrontation, and does not have an opinion on the disagreement between Kuwait and Iraq," stating that "We have no opinion on Arab-Arab conflicts". She told Saddam that the United States did not intend to "start economic war against Iraq."

This statement, quoted from the New York Times 23rd September 1990, may have given Saddam the green light to invade Kuwait.

At 2am on August 2nd 1990, the Invasion of Kuwait by Iraq began.

Chapter 2

Gerald Vincent Bull
8th March 1928 – 22nd March 1990

Gerald Bull was a Canadian-born astro-physicist by profession. He had dedicated his working life to producing and constructing a 'Supergun', which would be capable of firing satellites into space or launching artillery shells for thousands of miles. Subsequently, although his dream remained unfulfilled, it is acknowledged that his designs were amongst the most effective artillery designs world wide.

He held research contracts with the Canadian Department of Defence, McGill University and the United States Army.
The United States and the Canadian High Altitude Research Programme (H.A.R.P) gave him support to continue his research in 1962. Barbados was his original base. From there he used a small 5 inch gun to fire projectiles to an altitude of 70 kilometres. Projectiles fired from a 7 inch gun reached almost 100 kilometres. Due to his success, a larger HARP gun was produced in Arizona, by welding together two 16 inch battleship guns. The end product was a gun barrel of approximately 30 metres in length. When completed, the gun was used to disgorge light-weight projectiles.

On 19th November 1966, the gun did fire a 185 lbs projectile into space.

During the 1970's, Gerald Bull disassociated himself from the Pentagon. Described by some as a man of dubious character, he was imprisoned in the United States for 12 months in 1980, for breaching an arms embargo to South Africa.
The United States and Canadian governments withdrew their funding and support in 1967.

Upon his release, he set up several companies, and obtained agreements from the Iranian, Taiwanese, Chinese, and Chilean governments, amongst others. He formed his own company in Quebec, Canada. Through this company, and a Belgian subsidiary, he was able to construct the GC-45 gun, which had proven ability of being able to fire a shell to a distance of 25 miles. This gun was more powerful than any held by the armies of the western world.

After the Iraq-Iran war began in August 1988, the Iraqi Government took Bull by private aircraft from Geneva to Baghdad. This was the beginning of an association between Bull and the Iraqi Government, which was to last for almost 10 years. At this time, Saddam Hussein was Defence Minister in Iraq. It is known that Bull developed guns for South Africa and Libya, as well as the United States and Canada. Bull also modified missile warheads. These increased the range of Iraq's Scud Missiles. He extended his 'HARP' gun to increase the length of the barrel to 512 feet. Obviously the barrel would need to be segmented. Its capabilities would be to fire a 600 kilogram projectile, up to a range of 1,000 kilograms or, a 2,000 kilogram rocket-assisted projectile into space.

In July 1991, Iraq finally admitted that it did possess a gun which had a barrel 350 millimetres wide and 45 metres long. Iraq was also in the process of building a second gun. (Were the parts discovered, after an anonymous tip to British Customs officers, the missing parts? Or were the parts which I repaired at 'Forgemasters' the missing link?)

The United Nations Special Commission noted that this super-weapon would have been accurate for conventional weapons. It was also trying to assess whether or not the gun was intended for biological, nuclear or chemical usage.

General Hussein Kamel al-Majeed, a high ranking Iraqi defector said that the Iraqi's were working on a 'space weapon launched from the super gun. He is quoted as saying, "it was meant for long-range attack, and also to blind spy satellites. Our scientists were seriously working on that. It was designed to explode a shell into space that would have sprayed a sticky material on to the satellite and blinded it". He is also quoted as saying that "The super gun could have delivered a nuclear device".

The United Nations destroyed one 350 millimetre super gun, components of a 1,000 millimetre, and a super gun propellant.

There is no doubt, that the petro-chemical project was a front to purchase components from several companies, including 'Sheffield Forgemasters', by Iraq to assemble Bull's super gun.

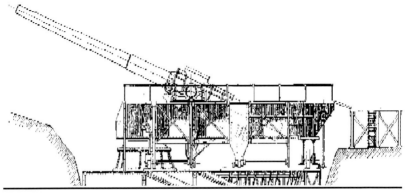

An artist's impression of Gerald Bull's 'Supergun.'

Matrix Churchill, a long established company based in middle England, was purchased by an Iraqi controlled company. Its speciality was the production machine tools. Acquisition of Matrix Churchill gave Iraq direct access to tooling, computer programming and components that would be needed to produce a wider variety of weapons.

Gerald Bull was found murdered outside his Brussels hotel, in March 1990. He died of gun shot wounds to the back of his head and neck. It is believed that Israeli agents were responsible.

Chapter 3
The first of Three Visits

In 1988 the City's most famous steel works, 'Sheffield Forgemasters, River Don Works' accepted what was to be the most controversial order in their history. Did their fame eventually become infamy?

This prestigious listed building is the Head Office of 'Sheffield Forgemasters'. The top floor is known as 'The Crystal Corridor, presumably because of the crystal chandeliers hanging in the Boardrooms.

Forgemasters were asked to produce two consignments of 26 pipes, to be installed as oil-carrying pipes for the 'Petro Chemical Oil Company' in Baghdad, Iraq.
However, my story begins two years later in January 1990.

Photograph of me on Brightside Lane Pointing towards Sheffield Forgemasters.

From September 1977, I was employed by a small engineering company, based at Attercliffe, Sheffield, in the very heart of the steel industry. Their main business was in specialised metal coatings. This process is known as metal spraying whereby, two continuous wires, located on coils, are passed simultaneously through a feeder 'gun'. The wires most commonly used are a mixture of mild steel and chrome. Under normal circumstances, metal spraying is used to build up worn surfaces, or as an exterior coating against corrosion and wear and tear.

At the point of arcing a jet of compressed air is introduced, projecting the pressurised and atomised molten metal forward, thus allowing variable thicknesses of coating to be built up over a period of time.

The Works Manager was Roy Wood. In my estimation, Roy was certainly one of the best metal sprayers in the country at that time. His experience and the quality of his work justified that title.

In late January 1990, Roy called me into his office, to discuss the company's latest project. He told me that we had been commissioned by 'Sheffield Forgemasters' to undertake some rectification work, and the meeting had been arranged for us later that day.

View from behind South Machine Shop, showing Forgemasters logo.

On our arrival, we were met by the Machine Shop Manager and their Engineering Consultant. This was not unusual, as we often worked 'on-site', when a job was too big for our own workshops, our capacity being a maximum of five tons.

We were escorted to what is now probably the world's most famous workshop, 'The South Machine Shop'. There we saw a horizontal borer, one of many, bearing a huge length of pipe, measuring 28 feet in length, five feet in diameter, with a bore of 39inches. It had flanges at each end. The flanges had a series of 2 inch bolt holes, which would allow further lengths of piping to be added. We were reminded that these pipes were part of a consignment of oil carrying pipes.

The Engineer explained that a crucial error had occurred during the final machining operation. The cutting tool had chipped, and gouged out a groove one inch wide by one eighth of an inch deep.

Although Roy Wood had discussed the job with Forgemasters, the look on his face was one of amazement. I can only assume that his expression must have mirrored my own. Very few jobs fazed us, but we agreed that this one would be 'one for the books'.

Several major hurdles would have to be overcome. The fact that the error had occurred almost half way down the pipe, was the main obstacle.

The second was which method should be chosen to ensure that an even deposit was laid down.

Thirdly, which one of us would be physically capable of remaining in an upright position inside the pipe; whilst it revolved at 5 revolutions per minute.
(R.P.M.) A complete revolution takes twelve seconds to complete.

Whichever method was chosen, would determine the ultimate success or failure. To fail would result in the loss of several thousands of pounds to Forgemasters, not withstanding the time lost in the production of another pipe.

These pipes were forgings not castings. Castings were not acceptable. The pipes had to be seamless in order to withstand extra pressure.

The decision of who would carry out the repair was easy. As I said earlier, Roy was a master of his craft, but we both knew that he was physically unable to do this job. Whilst on a walking holiday in Snowdonia the previous year, he had had a serious accident, resulting in long-term problems with his legs. I remember him looking at me sadly and saying, 'this one is up to you mate'. With this established, the final hurdle had to be resolved.

I am not the tallest of men at 5ft 8inch, but we still had to overcome the problems of keeping me upright as the pipe revolved, and being able to spray accurately.

We spent most of the day in the South Machine Shop, discussing the options and trying to foresee any obstacles that might arise.

It was decided that metal spraying was the only method that would ensure a perfect finish and would cause no distortion due to minimal heat. How I was going to be able to remain in a kneeling position for any reasonable length of time was the next problem.

Heavy Forge building as it is today.

At this point, we went back to our base, taking with us a long list for materials and the equipment needed, plus a couple of gigantic headaches.

This picture was taken in our workshops in 1986

Where the 'Arc' is visible, is where my colleague Brian Thompson's Swift centre borer was located.
{That's me in the bottom right hand corner.} The 'Rollers' at the fore of the photo belonged to the Kellogg's (Cornflakes) Company.

On the second day we returned, complete with the materials and equipment, the plan being that work would start on the third day.

Roy had pointed out that my rubber-soled safety boots would cause resistance, and restrict my ability to maintain an upright position.

We eventually agreed that if hessian sacks were placed in the pipe to form a carpet, just big enough for me to kneel on, I would be able to maintain the required position.

A length of rope was to be secured around my waist, and anchored to one end of the borer. Without the security of the rope, the momentum would have literally propelled me out of the chasm of the pipe or could have spun me around.

A cooling fan would be set up by the end of the bore. The merits of the fan were three-fold. In theory it would blow away the dust, the tremendous fumes and heat that would emanate from the inside of the bore. Subsequently the fan would be found to be useless, due to the intensity of the dust, fumes and overwhelming heat. That second day was also the day that I was going to practice working inside a revolving pipe. Had it ever been attempted? I honestly don't know, but I do know that I had personally never heard of it. I also know now that this was the most difficult job in all my thirteen years of metal spraying. I had never attempted anything remotely like it.

Admittedly, I didn't sleep too well that night, being very aware of the fact that the success of the job sat squarely upon my shoulders.

By the third day Roy and I were ready. Because of the importance of the task, but more importantly to monitor my safety, Roy was to stay with me until completion. He would also have to operate the spray plant. Being inside the pipe prohibited me from operating it myself.

Before leaving for Forgemasters that day, I had been discussing the job with my colleagues, all of whom were excellent and experienced Engineers.

The overriding fact that confused us was why, if this was meant to be an oil carrying pipeline, did the finish have to be so smooth and precise? Surely the constant gush of oil would smooth out and eradicate any imperfections.

On the short journey to Forgemasters, (approximately 1 mile away from our base) I discussed this with Roy. He agreed with me, but added it was of no importance to us. Our job was to comply with the customer's requirements, no more, no less.

Roy had already taken a full inventory of the equipment that would be needed. A `Metallization arc spray 200' spray plant was his choice, plus air hoses, shot blasting equipment and all the electrical connections that would be needed. The wire needed was 30/60, as a finishing coating, plus bonding wire. Our equipment was always tested on site before starting work. All the safety procedures had been followed, and the equipment was in place and ready to start.
All that remained was for me to don my safety goggles, fireproof gloves, overalls and respirator (an air-stream helmet). For the first time in my entire career, I had momentary doubts of my own ability. If things went wrong it could spell disaster for the job, tarnish my own and our firm's reputation and ultimately compromise my own safety. One wrong move on my part would result in me being badly burned, blinded, or both. In hindsight, I realised I could have been incinerated.

Roy would keep a constant view of me but it would have taken several seconds before he would have been able to switch off the power supply to the spray plant and even longer to stop the borer revolving. By that time, the damage would have been done. What if the spray plant broke down? Although it was checked on a daily basis, it had been known to malfunction.

These concerns were uppermost in my mind, and admittedly I was terrified. The weight of the responsibility was palpable.

I climbed into the great mouth of the pipe and allowed myself a couple of minutes to calm my screaming nerves. Roy too looked worried, although I knew that he trusted my ability implicitly. I was acutely aware of my responsibility, but my confidence had returned. I knew that my years of experience were equal to the job.

I had been taught to metal spray by Brian Thompson , a highly qualified and experienced Engineer. Brian had served his apprenticeship at English Steel Corporation, one of the former names used by Sheffield Forgemasters, River Don Works.

He had taught me well. Unfortunately, Brian had changed his employment before the Forgemasters jobs came up.

Here I am, inside the 'pipe', settling myself down as the boring machine began to revolve.

The borer was switched on and it began revolving slowly at first. I allowed myself time to adjust to the momentum.

A few of Forgemasters workforce had gathered, for they too had never seen such a spectacle. Someone called to me that I resembled a hamster running round in its wheel. I admit, I now have some empathy with hamsters

Within a few minutes I felt myself relax, and was in a reasonably comfortable position on my Hessian 'cushion'. Though a little cramped, it was time to make a start.

We had decided that although my cushion allowed a degree of comfort, we should allow the pipe to run with me inside, for about 20 minutes, to be absolutely sure that I maintained my kneeling position and sustain the momentum of 5 R.P.M. (Revolutions per Minute)

When we were satisfied that everything was as it should be, we stopped the boring machine, and Roy handed me the spray gun. Oddly enough all my nerves had disappeared, but this was no time to be overconfident. I certainly needed to call on all my years of experience and remain calm.

With my ear-defenders and goggles secured, the borer now being up to speed, running at 5 R.P.M and the spray plant switched on, I began to spray the molten metal into the damaged groove. I do remember glancing up and noticed that the work force had scattered. To them it must have resembled something out of a space movie. The purple glare from the arc shone out from each end of the pipe, causing a blinding flash of light.

Although my ear-defenders were of good quality, the noise was still deafening. The intense heat penetrated my flame-proof gloves. I signalled for Roy to switch off the plant.

After just ten minutes of spraying, I had become overwhelmingly hot and fatigued. We had hoped that I would be able to maintain a constant spray for at least twenty minutes before taking a cooling- off break.

It was obvious that I would need to take breaks at much shorter intervals. It was apparent that as I could only stay in-situ for ten minutes, it was going to be a long day. The job however, was proceeding exactly accordingly to plan.

The photograph above shows me Inside the 'pipe' at the moment when the borer began revolving and the spray plant was operating.
This picture appeared on the front cover of a well known welding magazine.

Whilst I cooled down, the inspectors did their job. I could see by their expressions that my work was up to the required standard. Although I felt very relieved, I knew that I couldn't afford to become blasé or over-confident. There was still a long way to go. Perfection was the only standard that they could allow. There was no margin for the slightest error on my part. Too much was at stake. The job and probably my safety were on the line.

I stayed with the routine of ten minutes spraying and ten minutes cool-off. Eventually, the groove was filled and the inspectors congratulated me on a job well done. The job had taken me approximately four hours overall.

It wasn't until Roy and I were back at our base, that I allowed myself a small element of pride. One thing was certain, if I never saw one of those pipes again, it would still be a month too soon.

Chapter 4
The Second Visit

I was back working at our base doing my routine work of spraying machine parts, mostly from local companies, including Forgemasters but sometimes on-site at Davy Roll Company at Gateshead, Northeast England.

The days were often lightened by the camaraderie of my colleagues. On one occasion, I was chosen to serve hot drinks.

These drinks were always appreciated. They not only quenched our thirst, but helped to reduce the dust which we inhaled and which also penetrated our protective clothing, (overalls)

(Please note that I didn't receive a bonus for my 'Extra Duties')

At around this time, a young man joined the company to be apprenticed in the art of metal spraying. He was bright, cheeky and cheerful, as are most eighteen year old lads. I was to teach him how to spray, and he was a willing and capable learner.

A couple of weeks later, we were called to 'Forgemasters' again. This time, it was to repair some small grooves in the flanges belonging to the newly repaired pipes. Until that time we were unaware of the existence of any flanges.

I decided to take the apprentice with me. (to ensure his privacy, I will call him Peter) It was his first experience of working on –site. We took our equipment with us. Roy had already viewed the job and we were to complete the repair within the day.

This picture, taken in our workshop was described by another colleague as being one of my better abilities.

The Engineer took us to a different building this time, which was fine by me. I had no wish to see those awful pipes again. Some were piled up, but others were already in crates marked, 'Petro-Chemical Oil Co, Baghdad'. The one that I had repaired lay there, waiting to be crated.

We stopped for Peter to examine it. He remarked, "That thing looks more like a gun barrel, rather than an oil pipe". Admittedly I had not considered this but laughingly agreed.

The repair didn't take too long as I used a tried and tested method of flashing rapid bursts of metal spray over the damaged areas , until enough had been deposited to allow the Engineers to grind the metal spray smooth enough to blend into the existing steel. With the task completed, we packed up our equipment and left.

Chapter 5
The Final Visit

For the next few weeks again, my work was just routine, metal spraying within our own workshops.

In early March 1990, the companies' services were again called by "Forgemasters" to another awkward job. On this, our third and final visit to "Forgemasters", another first class metal sprayer (I will call him Colin) was to accompany me, as this job necessitated continuous spraying, as well as being located in a restricted space.

All three of us, including my apprentice Peter, were taken not to the south machine shop, but to a smaller unit to the side. My colleague, Colin spotted the pipes and called the Forman over. Always outspoken, he told the Forman that, "these aren't parts of a pipe line, they're parts of a gun, I worked for another company and I have seen these things before". (for legal and security reasons, I am not allowed to name the company). The Forman remained adamant, and reiterated that they were parts of an oil pipe line. Colin also reminded the Forman that any member of staff not wearing a respirator would almost certainly be contaminated by the fumes.

Both Colin and I would be needed to do the spraying. The work proceeded as expected, both of us taking turns of 10 minutes on, and 10 minutes off. A longer period not only cause back pain, but would expose us to direct contact with the fumes. The compound to be used for this job was aluminium bronze. The putrid fumes are evil and dangerous. They contain cancer producing agents (carcinogenic). The colour of the arc from bronze is green.

The fumes that are sometimes inhaled almost always cause a sore throat, runny and painful eyes, a high temperature and in some cases, respiratory problems. In fact most of the symptoms associated with flu. Whenever we sprayed aluminium bronze on-site the work force regularly complained of feeling ill for a couple of days after, which is why it was decided that we would have to work over a weekend night.

Even allowing extra extraction, the filters in our respirators would have to be changed more frequently than was the norm.

It took eight hours of continuous spraying before the inspectors were satisfied that the deposit was an acceptable thickness.

I had never coated such a large area in aluminium bronze. It certainly wasn't my favourite compound. The three of us tattled down and left after what had been an exhausting night. Believe me, we were glad to breath fresh air again as we made our way home.

Back at our own base again, the final job at "Forgemasters" was often discussed around the table in the canteen. Colin still insisted that this was no ordinary pipe line. None of us ever returned to "Forgemasters".

I firmly believe that we were innocently embroiled in not only Saddam's "super gun" but Saddam's "super con"!

Had this third and final assignment for "Forgemasters" become the "missing parts" which was not only made in Sheffield but hidden in Sheffield.

To prove the point regarding contamination, I feel that I must digress slightly. A couple of years after I began working as a metal sprayer I began to show symptoms of flu. I would arrive home feeling shivery, headache and a sore throat and sometimes a high temperature. However, after a hot bath and good nights sleep, I would feel fine. I never missed a shift at work. These bouts of feeling unwell were to last for over twenty years. I am sure my wife, must have reached a stage were she didn't quite believe me. Who could blame her? I for one didn't know of anyone who got flu three times a week, but still put in a full weeks work. February 1998 was pretty awful; I had had this for flu for almost three weeks and just couldn't shake off the symptoms. I decided that it was time to visit my Doctor. Fortunately for me, he was what's known as a works' Doctor. He would visit companies and deal the work forces minor ailments. After a physical examination and many questions, he told me that he suspected that I had severe contamination. He called our local hospital and organised some test for me. These were blood and urine tests and several x-rays amongst numerous others. The other fortunate thing for me was that the hospital had recently set up a department which would deal with solely with respiratory problems which could be work related. I was tested for everything under the sun, including aids and many types of cancer. For nine weeks the tests and hospital visits were almost a daily routine. I did mention it to my employer who seemed quite confident that my health problems were not work related. Sadly, most of my colleagues appeared to agree, but agreed to be tested. I continued to work but one afternoon, my Doctor had telephone me expecting to find me at home. When my Wife told him that I was at work, he came and hauled me home with specific instructions of not to return. We all tested positive, and were finally diagnosed with chromium poisoning. Thank god that I showed no sign of any cancers.

After twelve weeks on sick leave, my employer contacted me and I informed me that it was obvious I would not be returning to work, they had no alternative but to sack me, or to quote their words "terminate my employment".
My colleagues continued to work until the company closed in 2004. My old chum "Colin" left shortly after me.

0.05 is the accepted level of chromium usually found within the human body, ingested mainly through the water supplies. My levels were 135. I was slowly killing myself. Unfortunately there is no cure for chromium poisoning. The only cure is to stay away from chrome. Chrome can only be excreted from the body by normal bodily function.

The good news is that after ten years my levels are normal. The bad news is that I lost a job which I love, not counting the friendships I had enjoyed for almost twenty years.

Chapter 6
Is It A Gun?

On April 12th 1990, all hell broke loose with a furore of television and newspapers headlines.

Sheffielder's were greeted by this headline in our local newspaper The 'Star'.

A Monster Gun or A Load of Old Pipes!!

For almost two weeks the news was relentless. As the facts were revealed, they became more alarming.

The news was especially bad for Sheffield. Had this great "Steel City" along with its master craftsmen, been dragged into a situation, un-paralleled since the terrible Cuban Crisis of 1962, when the world was again under a nuclear threat?

Arms Expert's Study 'Big Gun'.

It soon became apparent, that we had unknowingly made a contribution towards creating Weapons of Mass Destruction.

The Hierarchy at 'Forgemasters' were arrested. It was only by the intervention of a local Member of Parliament that Forgemasters Management were released without charge. The company I worked for was also interviewed but not arrested. Their files proved them to be totally innocent of any misdemeanour.

To our workforce, things had started to make more sense. Colin's theories had become a stark reality. It explained why the bore had to be so smooth, why such precision was needed for the flanges, and why some parts had to be sprayed with aluminium bronze. It is a scientific fact, that coating with this compound eliminates the possibility of sparks, all essential elements for the production of a superior gun.

'If it's a gun it must be kept away from Iraq' - Margaret Thatcher

INQUIRY DEMAND OVER PIPES

This was the headline and text printed in the Sheffield 'Star' on 16th April 1990.

Sheffield Member Of Parliament Bill Michie has called for an independent inquiry into the controversy surrounding city-made pipes alleged to form the barrel of the world's biggest gun.

His call comes as doubts and confusion continue over the eight cylinders said to form the 40-metre barrel of the so-called 'Iraqi Supergun' seized by Customs men at Teesport, Middlesborough on Wednesday. But Downing Street said the latest official position was as outlined by Mrs. Thatcher in Bermuda – it was still not clear what the piping was.

Bill Michie said that there was still confusion over the pipes - made by Sheffield 'Forgemasters'. He said," it has got to be an independent inquiry outside the Department of Trade and Industry, and hopefully get to the bottom of it".

Mrs.Thatcher, speaking in Bermuda yesterday after talks with President Bush, said if it WAS a gun barrel it should be kept out of the hands of the Iraqi government.

An Independent Television News report quoted unnamed senior Government sources as saying it was 'probably only a pipe' The Department of Trade and Industry, which cleared the export of The tubes, said it did not know who had made the comment to ITN.

Customs officials insist Ministry of Defence experts agree that the sections of piping seized at Teesport could be used in large artillery guns.

Local Members of Parliament insisted on the inquiry. One in particular ridiculed the Government, for not knowing what a gun looked like. Gordon Brown (current Chancellor of the Exchequer), also insisted on a full and immediate inquiry.

Margaret Thatcher, the Conservative Prime Minister at the time, defended her self by accusing 'Forgemasters' and Walter Somers Limited, of applying for the
WRONG LICENCES, adding that had they applied for the
RIGHT LICENCES, they would have been refused.

She also said that 'Forgemasters' and Walter Somers were aware that they were making parts for a gun. She had technically publicly accused both companies of knowingly breaking the law.

Had Thatcher made these comments outside the confines of the House of Commons, she would have left herself open to legal action by both firms. Was she covering her own back?

It is well documented that parts were produced by Forgemasters in Sheffield and a second company Walter Somers Ltd of Birmingham, West Midlands.

FULL UNIT OF PIPES IN IRAQ

17th of April saw this headline published by the 'Star', sparking off another chain of events. A consignment or 26 pipes (half the original order) was already in Iraq. Both companies were obliged to try to vindicate themselves.

A spokesman for 'Forgemasters' was quoted as saying that, 'One complete unit of 26 tubes, comprising of one assembly, weighing 402 tonnes and measuring 156 metres when connected up, had in fact been transported to Iraq.'

The second consignment of 26 pipes had been produced, but without 'The Screwed Ends'. Eight pipes had been seized by Her Majesty's Customs Officers at Teesside Docks in Middlesborough, North East England.

'BRITISH OFFICIALS KNEW ABOUT IRAQI SUPERGUN'

A report in the 'Star' said that British Intelligence knew about the existence of 'Supergun' for 19 months, before Customs Officials seized the parts made by a Sheffield Firm (Forgemasters).
It is quoted, that, Gerald Bull told both the Israeli and British Agents about the project in September 1988, in the hope of avoiding international action against it.

Interpol and British Customs Officers carried out searches throughout Europe, for British registered trucks, thought to be carrying further parts, in an attempt to deliver them overland to Iraq. Three trucks were eventually impounded, one in Greece, two more in Turkey.

Chapter 8

Journalists get Nosy

During this time, I was a member of a local Railway Preservation Group, a small group who shared a passion for railways. It was our intention to build a small narrow gauge line at our local park in the Rother Valley. To gain experience we often volunteered to help at various preserved railways up and down the country. Much time was spent, but unfortunately our plans never came to fruition.

At the Spring Bank Holiday at the end of May 1990, we were all down at Fairborn Railway Centre in Wales, who had invited the then Secretary for Wales to attend the naming ceremony for their new locomotive. The local press were there to cover the story.

Most of our group were down there, each of us taking up our assigned tasks. I was assigned to the peninsular, operating the points and signals for the loop line, but having no idea what was happening on the railway station.

Apparently the owner had mentioned to a journalist, that there was another "celebrity on sight" who had worked on Saddam's "Supergun", the name been used by the media. A couple of journalists came rushing over to me, notebooks at the ready asking me, 'Are you Roy? Did you know it was a gun? Surely you must have known?' Questions were coming at me in both directions. In all honesty, I didn't know how to answer them, so I just told them the truth. I had never worked on components for a gun, Saddam's or anyone else's.

I had repaired parts for a pipe line for "Petro Chemical Oil Company" it was obvious that they didn't believe me and they went away disgruntled. No newsflash for them that day
....

Chapter 9

Operation Desert Shield
And The Fall of Saddam Hussein

George Bush Senior., the 41st President of the United States of America, is known internationally, for his leadership of the United Nations coalition in the first Gulf War which took place between1990 - 1991. Saddam Hussein, President of Iraq, invaded Kuwait, the oil-rich country located south of Iraq in 1990. In an operation known as Desert Shield, it was the coalition's intention to remove the Iraqi forces from Kuwait, to ensure that they did not invade Saudi Arabia. Bush summarised his position by saying, "This aggression will not stand. This is not a war for oil. This is a war against aggression."

The United Nations passed a resolution in November, which established a deadline that authorised Kuwait's allies 'to use all necessary means' if Iraq had not withdrawn from Kuwait by January 1991.
January 17th 1991, saw the beginning of hostilities. American Air force Units launched a series of devastating attacks against Iraq. These attacks became known as "Operation Desert Storm." President Bush achieved his objectives of forcing an Iraqi withdrawal and therefore, liberating Kuwait. Hostilities ceased, and Saddam Hussein was allowed to remain in power. Bush's foreign policy would later be subjected to questioning.

The then Secretary of Defence, Dick Cheney had noted that in his opinion to invade the country would have quote, "got the United States bogged down in the quagmire inside Iraq." Bush's explanation as to why he did not order the overthrow of the Iraqi Government, quote, "It would have incurred incalculable human and political costs. We would have been forced to occupy Baghdad and, in effect rule Iraq."

President Bush later said, when offering his explanation to Gulf War veterans as to why he had chosen not to pursue the war further, "Whose life would be on my hands as the Commander in Chief because I, unilaterally, went beyond the international war, went beyond the stated mission, and said we're going to show our macho? We're going into Baghdad. We're going to be an occupying power- America in an Arab land – with no allies at our side. It would have been disastrous."

During and immediately after the apparent success of military operations in Iraq, President Bush's popularity ratings soared in America. Economic recession, combination with perceived failures about the end of the war later caused it to fall dramatically.

Unfortunately, the invasion did not rid the Iraqi people of their genocidal and tyrannical dictator. He was to remain in power until his capture and arrest in 2004.
Although subdued for a while, the Coalition still feared Saddam's capabilities.
When George W Bush came to power he had believed, as did his father before him, that Saddam still presented a threat to world peace.

2002 saw the start of the second Gulf War. It was the intention of Bush Junior and the coalition, to rid the world once and for all time of Saddam's Dictatorship, terrorism and the possibilities of Weapons of Mass Destruction.

Although the integral parts had remained in England, thanks to Britain's eagle eyed and diligent Customs Officers. Who knew for sure if Saddam had managed to obtain the 'Missing Parts' from another country? Today he faces the death penalty, but where would the world be if he had realised his dream of his new toy, which is still referred to to-day as 'Saddam's Supergun'.

SUPERGUN DEVICE HIDDEN IN CITY

(The Star's Headline "October 23rd 1991)

On this date, 'Sheffield Forgemasters' admitted; "We've still got part of the Iraqi Supergun". A piece of the sliding assembly, a 29.5 tonne steel tube, is lying at the 'Forgemasters' works where it was made.

Paul Ashwell, a British truck driver, had been arrested by Greek authorities in April last year. When arrested he was carrying an exact replica of the part remaining at 'Forgemasters'

Richard Caborn, a Member of Parliament for Central Sheffield, demanded that a United Nations team be called in to destroy it, like other parts of the Supergun already in Iraq.

It is understood that the remaining pipe hidden in Sheffield was locked away in a building at the River Don works. This integral part was to be the last part to be shipped to Iraq, and would have supported the rear part of the barrel when it recoiled after firing.

A 'Forgemasters', spokesman, which believed the tubes ordered by Iraq were for the Petro-chemical industry, admitted the part had been in its works 'since day one' of the Supergun affair. Although the Supergun and the tube, which remains in Sheffield, belong to the Iraqi government, 'Forgemasters' has been paid for its work.

I am now convinced that the forging that we had coated with aluminium bronze, was in fact, a breech for Supergun.

Chapter 11
Margaret Thatcher

It seems that Margaret Thatcher had pressurised W.H. Bush into driving Saddam Hussein's army out of Kuwait. This Pressure was to be one of her final acts as Conservative Prime Minister of the United Kingdom. Bush was apprehensive about the attack, but Thatcher famously told him, "This is no time to go wobbly".

It is strongly believed that the reason for going to war was purely political. Could it be wholly coincidental that after the war ended, Thatcher's only son, Mark made his fortune by selling prohibited arms to South Africa? He was find a total of equivalent of $500,000 and given a suspended sentence of four years. He Vehemently insisted that when he agreed to finance a helicopter in South Africa, it was to be used as an air ambulance.

Mark Thatcher made a plea bargain and said in his statement that "There is no price too high to pay to be re-united with my family. I am sure that all of you who are husbands and fathers would agree.

His mother was the first and only female ever to serve as Prime Minister of the United Kingdom. She is also the longest serving Prime Minister in the last 150 years. She remained in office for 11 years (1979-1990).

On November 22nd 1999, she was forced to retire by her Government, who had refused to back her.

Chapter 12
Conclusion

The Iraqi government was outraged and warned of a possible trade war in retribution for the allegations. They still insisted that the pipes were part of their oil pipeline.

British Customs Officers agreed that Iraq may have intended to use the first consignment as part of their pipeline, but added that they believed the second consignment was for pipes to make up a gun, the steel used in the manufacture of the pipes was an American brand, known as HY80, and could be used for armament components.

Although completed Weapons of Mass Destruction were never found, it has been proved that if assembled, Saddam Hussein's regime would have built what would without a doubt, have been one of world's deadliest weapons. The assembled components would have the capabilities of becoming not one, but two guns which may have had the potential to fire nuclear shells. The scale of destruction and loss of innocent lives is incalculable.

Fortunately the integral components (some breeches and pipes) remained in England I have no doubt in my mind now that, the work we carried out on aluminium bronze was on one of the breeches. Without a breech it would have been impossible to construct an intended gun. The huge number of pipes would have been needed, not necessarily to extend the length of the barrel, but to replace the 'Leader' pipe. It is accepted that the number one pipe would need to be replaced; such was the pressure of a would-be projectile. Its projection would cause immediate damage to the leader barrel. This information was revealed in a television documentary.

The skill of the Forgemen and machinists is still undeniable. These huge forgings would have surely been a test of their skills.

I am confident that if they look back in hindsight, they would be relieved that for once, the machine 'went wrong'. It's inconceivable to consider the consequences if they had 'clocked off' their shift that day and said, 'The jobs a good un' (an old Sheffield saying).

SUPERGUN DESTROYED

A United Nations official said That Iraq had destroyed its Monster Supergun. The picture below shows Sabah al- Khafaji at his bus factory in Iskandariya, 30 miles south of Baghdad, with scrap barrels from Saddam's Supergun.

Patrice Palanque said that he had watched the destruction of the gun before leaving Iraq.

Saddam Hussein was detained in the custody of the Americans until his controversial Trial which began in July 2005. He faced charges 'against humanity'.

He was found guilty on all charges. His punishment was the death sentence Saddam insisted that as his heinous crimes were of a military nature, and that he should be afforded the dignity of facing a firing squad. His appeal was refused. He would be hanged.

He was handed over to the Iraqi Government on December 29th 2006 at 03:00hrs Baghdad time, the following morning he was hanged. Some British Government Ministers, including Gordon Brown, described the event as deplorable.

In his comments on the execution, G.W Bush Junior said, "That although the manner of Saddam Hussein's execution was despicable, Justice had been served."